I AM ME
I AM KELSEY

LA'SHANA M. KIRKSEY
ILLUSTRATIONS BY MICAELA STÉFANO

Copyright page

Cover design and illustrations by Micaela Stefano
Book design by Alejandro Martin

ISBN:
Hardcover ISBN: 978-1-7370955-2-1
Paperback ISBN: 978-1-7370955-0-7
eBook ISBN: 978-1-7370955-1-4

This is dedicated to all the little girls who are beautiful just the way you are. Also, to Rosevelt and Cheryl Kirksey for always motivating me to be the best version of myself! I couldn't ask for a better support system than my parents.

Hi, I am Kelsey!

Sometimes,
other kids laugh at me
because I do not look like
kids on social media.

6

It makes my eyes fill with tears,
and my tummy turn over.

So, I just go to my room
and never want to leave!

I lay on my bed and think
about the not-so-nice things
the kids say about me.

They say my size
is not small enough to fit in with them.

But I am me!

They say my clothes
are not in style right now.

But I am me!

They say my glasses make me look like
I should work in a lab doing experiments.

But I am me!

They say my hair
makes me look like a baby.

But I am me!

My size is what makes me extra special!

My clothes make me
stand out in a crowd!

My glasses make my eyes
sparkle like a unicorn's horn!

My hair is naturally beautiful,
and I can change how it looks
every day!

It's never nice for someone
to make fun of how you look.

Sometimes,
I forget that I am beautifully made.

Other kids might tease me,
but they are beautifully made, too!

Lift your head up and smile!
I will always be me, and you
should always be you because
that is all we can do!

"Never forget just how beautiful you are. Stand tall and smile!"

La'Shana M. Kirksey

About the Author

La'Shana M. Kirksey is an educator in Detroit, Michigan. She absolutely loves working with children! When she is not teaching or writing a book, she is spending time with her family and friends. Her favorite color is pink, and she would wear it every day if she could. Her favorite food is any kind of spicy food! Arcades is her favorite place to go and she really believes she can beat anyone at Go Kart. She plans to keep writing books to lift children up and love who they are.

I AM ME
I AM KELSEY

CPSIA information can be obtained
at www.ICGtesting.com
Printed in the USA
LVHW071927240621
691047LV00002B/65